Sylwedyth

written by Steve Wharton
illustrated by Mike Hartley

Contents

Chapter One

Cogo tells a story of the Sun

Once upon a hillside, thousands of years ago but not very far away from here, a girl called Sylwedyth sat with her friends and family. In a circle around a bright, hot fire, they were listening to a man called Cogo telling a story.

With one hand flat in front of his chest to show the land, Cogo held his drum with his other hand and used it to symbolise the sun rising.

'Some tribes believe the sun is newly born every morning. It grows from being a baby to a child. Then from a child to a strong queen and finally it becomes a frail old woman. They believe it dies every evening and that the birth and death of the sun create the day and the night.'

Cogo paused for dramatic effect with his drum held low to the ground. Some of the villagers jiggled with anticipation. Sylwedyth couldn't tell if they were cold or excited as she heard sharp intakes of breath between toothy smiles.

It looked as if Cogo had turned to stone. His still, dark figure lit by firelight

'Some say that as Lugh works at his forge to make weapons for the other gods, every beat of his hammer sends a hundred colours out into the sky: red, yellow, blue, orange, purple, pink, green and some colours that the living can't even see!

'But the sun is not the only fiery furnace in the sky. Every ancestor is given a forge to work. Every night you can see them burning in the sky. But they all fade away when Lugh returns with his great fire to start the new day.'

Cogo turned towards a gap in the hills and raised his hands to the sky as the sun rose over the village once more.

Chapter Two

Sylwedyth looks for weather signs

Sylwedyth liked the story but needed to ask Cogo a question.

'Is the story about Lugh's fire in the sky true?'

'It's as true as the moon follows the sun,' Cogo replied. 'Everything that our ancestors knew has been passed to us in sayings, from mother to daughter and father to son.'

Sylwedyth had heard lots of these sayings but couldn't remember many. She spent the next few days asking everyone around the village to tell her some.

Most of the sayings were about whether it would rain or not. Each time someone told her a saying such as 'red sky at night, no rain tonight,' she would ask if it was true. 'As true as the moon follows the sun,' would be the reply.

She asked her father for a saying about the weather. He told her when the spider leaves its spinning, it means that rain is beginning.

'Is it true?' she asked.

'As true as the moon follows the sun,' he replied with great certainty.

If the cockerel goes crowing to bed,
he'll certainly rise with a watery head.

When clouds look like black smoke,
a wise man will put on his cloak.

When leaves show their undersides,
be very sure that rain it betides.

Not all of the sayings were about rain. She heard one about knowing when it would be night time:

When the dandelion covers its head,
soon it will be time for bed.

There was another about the weather getting colder:

When bright stars are shining,
the firewood you should be piling.

Every time she asked if a saying was true, the reply was always the same: as true as the moon follows the sun.

Sylwedyth started to watch for the spiders leaving their spinning, and listened for cockerels crowing at night. The things mentioned in the sayings were all around her but she still didn't know if the sayings were true.

She decided to make a tool to help her keep track of how often the sayings were true.

If she saw a black cloud then she would tie a knot in a piece of thin rope. If it rained soon after she'd tie a piece of wool next to it. If it didn't rain, she wouldn't tie wool next to it.

Sylwedyth made knotted ropes for the many sayings she had heard and soon had a whole library of weather information hanging from her belt.

She found that if she relied only on one saying, it would be right only some of the time. Such as, if a spider left its web then sometimes it would rain, sometimes it wouldn't.

As she looked around and up at the sky she saw a curious thing: the moon. The moon in the daytime, high in sky. Behind it, rising up, following the moon... was the sun.

'But the moon follows the sun', thought Sylwedyth. 'Doesn't it?'

She stopped watching for rain. For the next few days and nights she observed the moon and the sun.

Looking at the sun hurt her eyes. It was too bright to look at, even for a short time. So she made another tool.

She boiled an old sheep's horn in water for a few hours. Then she flattened it by hitting it with a round rock. Sylwedyth couldn't see through the horn like we can see through glass. When she held it up to the sun, the light was strong enough for her to see a yellow circle in the middle of the flattened horn but it didn't hurt her eyes anymore. She saw that the sun was following the moon. And they were getting closer.

Holding her fingers at arm's length to measure the gap between the sun and the moon, Sylwedyth checked then double checked that what she thought was happening was right. She knew she had to tell the rest of the village.

'Everybody look at the sun. It's going to run into the moon!' They all looked up and sure enough, through squinted eyes and by borrowing Sylwedyth's flattened horn, they saw the sun and moon touch.

Cogo cried, 'It's the end of the world! Our ancestors left a saying about this happening:

When Lugh's fire turns black,
Heat and light we will lack,
If these gifts he cannot send,
Then our life on land will end!'

The moon looked like it was eating the sun. Daylight began to fade. Shadows on the ground grew thinner and the birds stopped flying. A butterfly landed on Sylwedyth's arm and went to sleep. A huge black disc hung in the sky.

The world did not end. But it did get quieter. For a few minutes it was night time again.

Then, slowly, it got brighter. Shadows thickened and the birds sang their dawn chorus for the second time that day.

Sylwedyth waited for the butterfly to wake up and flutter away. It gave her time to think.

Cogo said the ancestors had passed the sayings down to us. If there's a saying about the sun growing dark, then our ancestors must have seen it happen before.
Did the world end then?
No, it didn't.

Sylwedyth decided to start some new observations.

Chapter Four
Sylwedyth builds the first stone circle

'I don't understand it,' said Cogo. 'The saying about Lugh's fire going dark is as true as the moon follows the sun.'

'The moon doesn't follow the sun!' shouted Sylwedyth. 'There are times when the moon is high in the sky and the sun is only just rising. I don't know why but I'm going to find out.'

'We will ask Lugh,' announced Cogo. 'I will blacken three bones from a sheep's back in the fire, rub their soot all over my body and eat cow poo until Lugh speaks to me.'
'Do what you want,' snapped Sylwedyth. 'I'm going to find the answer my way: by observing.'

From that moment she spent every day watching the Sun and Moon rise and set.

She laid rope on the ground pointing in the direction of the sunrise but it was easily blown away. Marks she made in the soil with a stick disappeared after heavy rain. The small stones she piled up got kicked around by sheep and horses.

Eventually she asked her brothers to bring her a big stone. It was as high as Sylwedyth but much, much heavier.

They rolled it to the top of her weather watching hill and she used it to mark the direction in which the sun had risen that day.

For the next few years, from the middle of an almost full circle of stones, Sylwedyth watched the sun rise and set.

From doing this she learned that in the summer, when the days were long and hot, the sun rose from behind the flat-topped mountain, climbed high in the sky and then set behind the island in the sea.

In winter, when the days were shorter and colder, the sun climbed only as high as two hands above the horizon. It rose over the grasslands and set near the mouth of the river.

Using her stone circle, Sylwedyth knew when it was the middle of summer and the middle of winter because on those days the sun rose in the same place for five days in a row.

She had made a calendar and discovered what we now call the Summer Solstice and Winter Solstice.

She told the rest of the village and they were happy.

Because they knew when the hot summer days were going to get shorter and when the cold winter days would get longer, the villagers could plan when to plant seeds and when to harvest crops.

At each of those special times they would celebrate.

Cogo would sing the song about Lugh's fire and the villagers would dance.

Sometimes the dancers looked a lot like flowers opening and closing their petals, and turning their heads around to follow the sun.

Sylwedyth kept watching the sky and added more stones to her circle to line up with important times for some of the stars.

She still enjoyed listening to Cogo's stories, but she liked observing the world around her even more.

And by my fingers and thumbs, this story is...

done!

Stone Circles to visit in Cumbria

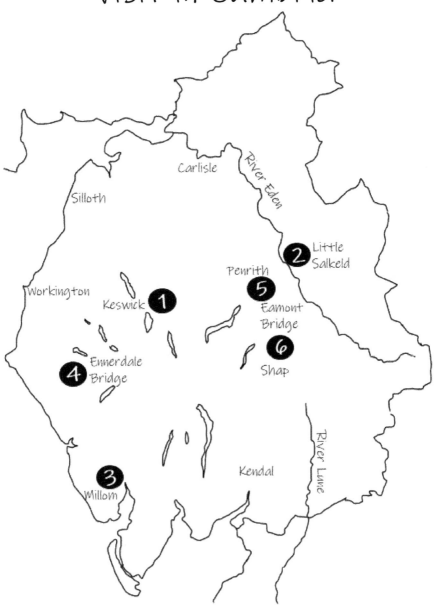

1 Castlerigg is one of Britain's oldest stone circles. It has 38 stones. They have been in place for more than 5000 years.

2 Long Meg and Her Daughters is a stone circle with a legend attached: the stones were once witches who were cursed by a wizard. It is also said that a person cannot count the stones twice and get the same number. Long Meg is the tallest stone. It is 3.6metres high and has art carved on its sides.

3 Swinside Stone Circle hides on a hill above Millom. It is made of 55 slate stones. Two of the stones are a gateway for watching the sun rise on the Summer Solstice.

4 Kinniside Stone Circle looks ancient but it might have been created in the late 1800's by a cheeky Victorian who took big stones from nearby farms. You can often find lots of horses visiting the stone circle.

5 Mayburgh Henge is a single, massive stone surrounded by a circular bank built using stones from the nearby River Yanwath. It is easy to imagine important meetings between kings and sports events taking place here.

6 Oddendale Stone Circle near Shap has two circles of stones. An inner circle and an outer circle. They are not very high but they are great for a picnic.

Why the Moon doesn't follow the Sun

When standing on the Earth, it looks like the Sun and Moon move around us. This is what people thought for a long time, but it isn't 100% true.

The Earth travels around the Sun. The path it takes is called its orbit. It takes one year for the Earth to go all the way around the Sun.

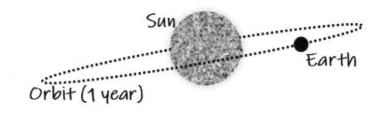

As it travels, the Earth is also spinning. It takes 24 hours for one full spin.

We don't notice the Earth spinning when we're stood on it so it looks like the Sun is moving around us.

The Moon moves around the Earth. It takes 27.3 days to complete one full orbit.

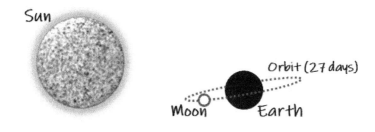

From our spinning Earth, it looks like the Sun and Moon travel along the same path in the sky: rising in the East, reaching their highest point to the South and setting in the West.

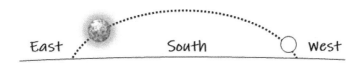

Although the Sun comes up in the morning and goes down in the evening, the movement of the Moon is not related to the Sun. In fact, the Moon moves across our sky more slowly than the Sun. Moonrise tomorrow will be later than it is today.

However, we are more likely to notice the Moon when the Sun has set. Which is why the people in Sylwedyth's village might have believed that the Moon followed the Sun.

Shadows

A shadow is made when something blocks light. Look at the ground on a sunny day; you, me, trees, dogs and lots of other things have shadows. This is because we have stopped the some of the sunlight from reaching the ground. As we move, the shadows move.

Hold your hand 30cm away from a wall and shine a torch at it to make a shadow on the wall. Wiggle your fingers. What does the shadow do?

Shadows will also change their length and shape when the light moves. What happens to the shadow of the box as the sun moves lower in the sky?

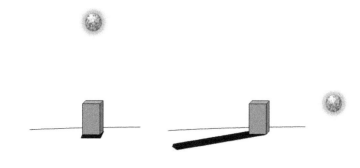

When people were first starting to tell the time, they used shadows to help them. They would mark out where a stick in the ground cast its shadow at different times of day. These simple clocks are called sundials.

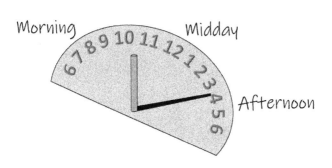

In Summer, the Sun climbs much higher in the sky than in Winter. It also rises further East and sets further West.

What do you think shadows will look like in the Winter, when the Sun is lower in the sky?

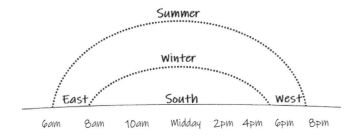

Seasons

The Earth is lazy. It doesn't stand up straight. It's axis (the imaginary line between the North Pole and South Pole) leans over by 23 degrees. That's a little bit bigger than one pizza slice if you cut the pizza into eight slices.

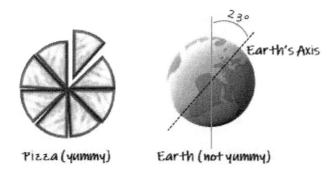

Pizza (yummy)   Earth (not yummy)

Because of this tilt, for six months of the year the top half of the Earth (Northern Hemisphere) gets lots of sunlight. The days are longer than the nights. This is Summer.

In Winter, when the top half of the Earth is leaning away from the Sun it gets less sunlight. The nights are long. It gets colder. This is Winter.

Solstice and Equinox

Twice every year there is a day when the day and night are the same length. These days are called the Spring Equinox and Autumn Equinox.

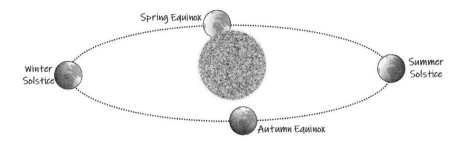

Using her stone circle, Sylwedyth saw that something else special happens twice a year. The Sun rises and sets in the same place for around 5 days. These days are the Summer Solstice and Winter Solstice.

Each of the Equinox and Solstice days are signs that the seasons are changing: Winter to Spring to Summer to Autumn and back to Winter again.

These days were very important for the people who built stone circles and sometimes one or two of the stones in the circles line up with where the Sun will rise on one of these days.

The Changing Moon

As the Moon orbits the Earth, it looks like the Moon changes shape. This is because the Moon always has a light side and a dark side. The Moon does not make its own light. We can see it because light from the Sun bounces off it.

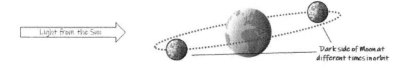

When we look at the Moon at different times in a month, it looks like it has changed shape. This is how the Moon looks from the Earth over 4 weeks.

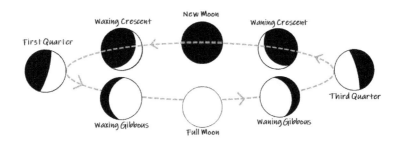

When the Moon is at its darkest it is called a New Moon. Then we see a Crescent Moon growing bigger (waxing) until it is a Full Moon. After that it gets thinner again (waning).

What is an Eclipse?

The Sun is much further away from Earth than the Moon. This means the Sun and Moon could never crash into each other like Cogo feared.

As the Moon orbits the Earth sometimes it can block the Sun's light. When the Moon's shadow falls on the Earth it is called a Solar Eclipse. From the Earth it looks like the Moon is covering up the Sun.

If you are not under the darkest part of the shadow (Umbra) then you will see a Partial Solar Eclipse made by the lighter part of the shadow (Penumbra).

When the Earth's shadow falls on the Moon it is called a Lunar Eclipse. The Moon turns red!

Are you a scientist?

There are many names for scientists depending on what they like most. However, all scientists use the same basic skills: observing and measuring.

Instead of accepting that 'the Moon follows the Sun', Sylwedyth observed the movements of the Sun and the Moon herself. Not just for day, but over a long time. By doing this she could see patterns in the movements.

Even today, there are a lot of differences in the way that people measure things. Depending on where you are, you might use inches, feet, pints, gallons, ounces, pounds and Fahrenheit. This is called the Imperial System and it can be difficult to remember how the measurements relate to each other.

In the late 18th century, French scientists and mathematicians developed a new way of measuring based on tens, hundreds and thousands: the Metric System; metres, litres, grams, volts and Celsius. They even tried a system of having 10 days in every week!

Because of all the simple steps we have taken in science, we know amazing things about the Sun, the stars and the Universe.

We know it takes eight minutes for light to travel to us from the Sun. That's because it's 150 million kilometres away!

Our Sun is so big that 109 Earths would fit side-by-side across its middle. Because it's so big it has enough gravity to keep all of the planets in our solar system spinning around it.

We now have cameras in space looking at the sun, stars and planets all the time. It's amazing but it wouldn't be possible without people inventing satellites... or space rockets to get the satellites into space... or telescopes... or glass for making lenses for telescopes... or tools for measuring. Which is what Sylwedyth did with her knotted cord and stone circle.

What will you invent?

Even small inventions can have a big impact.

Read the following bonus story to find out how...

The Sun King and the Scientists

King Louis XIV (the fourteenth) of France used the Sun as his symbol to show people how important he was.

In the year 1710, King Louis gathered his best advisors together to ask which scientist had made the most important discovery about the Sun.

His advisors argued for different people from many different countries. One advisor suggested Hipparchus, a man born in Turkey, nearly 2000 years ago.

Hipparchus divided the circle into 360 degrees and made a quadrant, a tool that can measure how many degrees above the horizon the sun is.

Another advisor spoke up saying that Galileo, from Italy was the most important. 100 years ago, Galileo was the first person to make a telescope and to point it at the sky. He also made the first thermometer to measure heat.

The last advisor to speak told the king that Isaac Newton, an Englishman, just 30 years ago invented a telescope that can see further than any other because it has mirrors inside it.

He also used a prism to split white light into all the colours of the rainbow and measured the temperature of each one.

It's because of him we also know that there is some light that people cannot see, called ultraviolet and infrared.

'I will have to read more about these great scientists and their ideas before I decide which of you will become my chief advisor in matters of science. Page boy, bring me my spectacles!'

The page boy brought the royal cushion with the King's spectacles and said, 'Excuse me your Highness, I have added arms to glasses that hook behind your ears so that the glasses do not fall off your face. It means that you can read for longer without your arms getting tired from holding up your glasses. You can now hold your book and drink a cup of coffee at the same time.'

'Amazing!' shouted King Louis. He turned to his advisors, 'You have told me about many great minds and inventions, but my page boy has invented something so simple and yet so clever that I will make him my chief advisor in matters of science.'

The page boy became a scientist himself, learning everything he could find in books in the royal library. And although he now had a very busy job and had to be able to explain some very big ideas to the king, he always made sure to give just as much attention to the little ideas too.

And by my fingers and thumbs,
    this story is...
                    done!